Primary Specials!

Tudor Times

Mary Green

Folens Publishers

© 2003 Folens Limited, on behalf of the author

United Kingdom: Folens Publishers, Apex Business Centre, Boscombe Road, Dunstable, LU5 4RL
Email: folens@folens.com

Ireland: Folens Publishers, Greenhills Road, Tallaght, Dublin 24
Email: info@folens.ie

Poland: JUKA, ul. Renesansowa 38, Warsaw 01-905

Editor: Dawn Booth   Layout artist: Suzanne Ward

Illustrations: Tony Randall   Cover design: Martin Cross

Cover image by permission of The British Library, Add. 42130, image no. 8388655

First published 2003 by Folens Limited.

British Library Cataloguing in Publication Data. A catalogue record for this publication is available from the British Library.

ISBN 1 84303 059 4

Contents

Other Titles

We hope that you enjoy using this new *Primary Specials!* book, which has been written in response to market research with teachers who told us that photocopiable activity books are needed to provide materials at different levels for use with lower ability students.

New *Primary Specials!* contain 15 separate chapters, each covering a new topic within the theme of the pack. Material is then structured to give teachers:

- Notes on how and when to use the topic in their scheme planning.
- Background details to provide extra context to the teacher for the topic and activity.
- Guided notes on working with each activity sheet.
- Guidance on points to consider when completing activities.
- A selection of useful questions to consider when discussing the topic.

Why not look for these other titles in the series?

Ancient Egypt	FC0616
Ancient Greece	FC0640
Children in Victorian Britain	FC0624
Children in the Second World War	FC0608
Invaders and Settlers in Britain	FC0586
How Life Has Changed Since 1948	FC0632

Can't find the topic your are looking for? If you have any ideas for other titles to be covered in the *Primary Specials!* series write and let us know:

Publishing Department
Folens Publishers
Unit 20
Apex Business Centre
Boscombe Road
Dunstable
Beds LU5 4RL

Nobles and Gentry

Background

The court was at the top of the social strata in Tudor England closely followed by nobles and then by the gentry. Portraits of the period show us what the rich wore. However, these were created to display wealth and it is likely that everyday wear was plainer than the costumes presented in portraits. During Henry VIII's reign, broadly speaking, a man would wear a padded doublet, short coat or tunic, woollen hose and a hat, often with a feather. A woman would wear a long wide-sleeved gown over a kirtle (an outer petticoat) and a head-dress called a coif. She would also wear a corset, petticoat and chemise; sleeves were often slashed to reveal some of these fine undergarments. Ermine and jewels might be added to velvet and silk as a sign of wealth.

Fashion during the Elizabethan period was similar but more exaggerated. The bodice on women's gowns became longer and farthingales (dress hoops) and bumrolls (padding at the hips) were used. For men, short, padded breeches and cloaks were added to the doublet and hose. The ruff was also an important fashion item for both men and women, and perfume and decorated pomanders were hung round a woman's girdle, or attached to a chain on a man, to disguise offensive smells.

Working with the resources

'A wealthy woman' and 'Changing fashions'

These two resource pages can be used together to discuss changes in Tudor fashion. The first shows a noblewoman at the time of Henry VIII, and the second a noblewoman during the Elizabethan period.

Useful questions

'A wealthy woman'

1 What kind of gown is the woman wearing?
2 What do you think it is made of?
3 How many layers can you see?
4 What has she got on her head?
5 What jewellery is the woman wearing?
6 What has she got round her waist?

'Changing fashions'

1 In what way is the Elizabethan costume different from the Tudor one?
2 How is it similar to the Tudor one?
3 What do you think the gowns were like to wear?
4 How are they different from the clothes girls wear today?

Using the activity sheet

'Compare the two'

The children can use the activity sheet to compare the two illustrations. The frame at the bottom of the page will help them to note the difference between Tudor and modern clothes.

A wealthy woman

A wealthy woman – a noblewoman during Henry VIII's reign

PRIMARY SPECIALS! *Tudor Times*

Changing fashions

Changing fashions – a noblewoman in Elizabethan times

Compare the two

Look again at 'A wealthy woman' and 'Changing fashions'.

● How are they different?
● How are they similar?

Finish the chart below. The first has been done for you.

Not the same	The same
In 'Changing fashions' there is a neck ruff.	Both dresses look heavy.

Think of three ways that they are different from girls' clothes today.

Today the clothes girls wear are made from _____

They are also _____

My third point is _____

Trades and Occupations

Background

The social structure of the Tudor period was hierarchical and closely defined, and it was accepted by most people. The nobility and gentry came under the court forming the professional classes – merchants and yeoman (rich farmers). These were followed by the husbandmen, apprentices, servants and labourers, and finally there were the poor and the beggars. The vast majority of people were at the lower end of the scale.

Life was uncertain; it was easy to fall, even from comparative comfort to near beggary, as a result of an inability to work through illness or accident or through a succession of poor harvests. Society was labour intensive and the majority of people, including women, worked on the land. Women also ran the home. There was also a range of trades and jobs, from farrier to hawker, to cover most needs and it was common practice to have more than one job to supplement earnings.

Using the activity sheets

'What are their jobs?'

The children should have grasped, through discussing the above questions, what the jobs shown in the Tudor street scene are, particularly the unfamiliar ones. The activity sheet will give you some idea whether or not they have.

'What would you ask?'

This is a question-setting exercise that challenges the children to ask suitable questions. All the answers should be found in the picture. They can then give their questions to another child to answer. They will need 'A Tudor street scene' to complete the grid, and you may need to remind them to add question marks to their sentences.

Working with the resource

'A Tudor street scene'

This street scene depicts a range of trades, jobs and situations that can be discussed with the children. You may need to explain most of the trades: particularly the cooper (a barrel and cask maker), weaver, printer, shepherd, carrier (someone who carried goods from one place to another in a cart), brewer, dairy maid, tanner, farrier (a blacksmith who shoes horses). Some of the children may have surnames that match the trades and this could be a further discussion point.

Useful questions

1 What does the main picture show us?
2 What are the traders selling?
3 What else is happening?
4 What are the streets like?
5 Can you tell who is poor and who is rich? How?
6 Try to work out what the trades are in the smaller pictures.

A Tudor street scene

A Tudor street scene

PRIMARY SPECIALS! *Tudor Times*

What are their jobs?

Can you remember what the people in the following jobs do?
Match them to their meanings by drawing a line.
The first has been done for you.

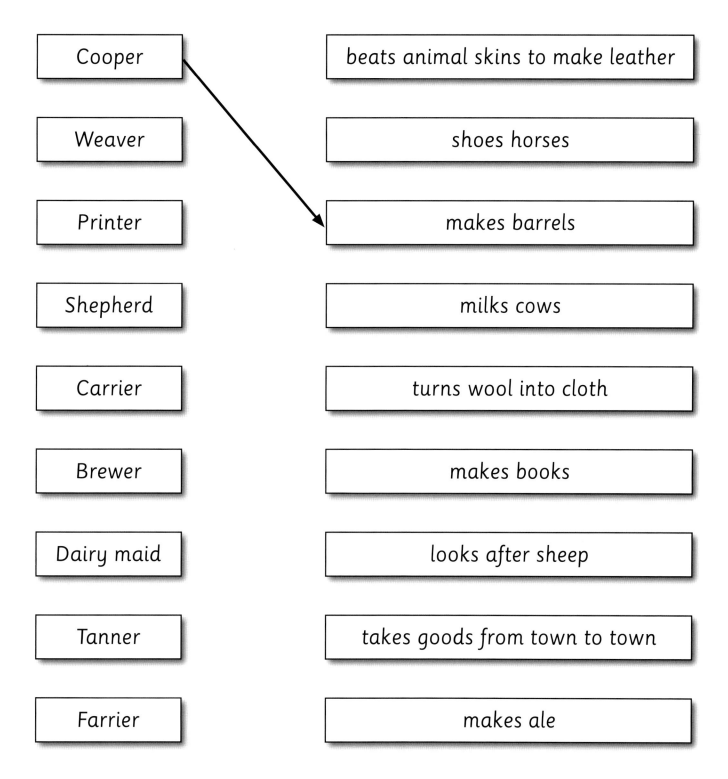

Cooper	beats animal skins to make leather
Weaver	shoes horses
Printer	makes barrels
Shepherd	milks cows
Carrier	turns wool into cloth
Brewer	makes books
Dairy maid	looks after sheep
Tanner	takes goods from town to town
Farrier	makes ale

What would you ask?

Look at 'A Tudor street scene'.

1 Write down a question to ask each of the following people about their jobs. Try to make sure that for each one the answer is in the picture. The first has been done for you.

Shoemaker *What do you make your shoes from?*
Beggar
Flower seller
Carpenter
Cooper
Butcher

2 Now ask a friend to answer your questions.

The Great Tudor Houses

Background

With the dissolution of the monasteries and the redistribution of land to the nobles, there was a desire for grand houses to be built. Henry VIII built and furnished more than any other monarch. Many skilled European craft workers came to England during the Tudor period. They were attracted by Henry's numerous building projects and his support for the arts.

Great houses and palaces would employ stewards, yeoman, servants and peasants; entire villages might be given over to their maintenance. Conversely, the whole village of Cuddington was destroyed to make way for Nonsuch Palace, built between 1538 and 1547, with the dissolved Merton Priory providing the rubble for the foundations. Nonsuch Palace was largely medieval in style, turreted and decorated with tracery, carvings and gilt. However, it also included a startling series of roman gods and goddesses and classical scenes. Its name, Nonsuch (non pareille), means 'without equal'. It was used only occasionally by Elizabeth I and was demolished in 1682.

Using the activity sheets

'Choose the words'

Here the children can use what they have learned to select the appropriate words for each building, as follows:

- **Nonsuch Palace:** stone, brick, dark, cold, damp, fancy, arches, towers, larger
- **Sunlight House:** glass, steel, concrete, light, warm, plain, flat roof, sunroof, smaller

'Living in Nonsuch Palace'

The frame should help the children to record the earlier discussion about what it would be like to live in Nonsuch Palace; why they would like or dislike living there and how others might differ in their opinion. They can use some of the words from 'Choose the words'.

Working with the resource

'Nonsuch Palace and Sunlight House'

The children could identify some of the differences between Nonsuch Palace and the modern Sunlight House, placing them historically and trying to guess what building materials were used. The basic materials for Nonsuch Palace were stone, brick and timber, while the modern house is made of concrete, glass, steel and timber.

Useful questions

1 Which building do you think Henry VIII built? Why?
2 What do you think Nonsuch Palace is made from?
3 What do you think it was like to live in?
4 Do you think Sunlight House was built at the same time as Nonsuch Palace or not? If not, when do you think it was built?
5 What do you think Sunlight House is made from?
6 Do you think any of the materials in Sunlight House might be the same as those in Nonsuch Palace?
7 How is Sunlight House different from the palace?
8 Which would you prefer to live in? Why?

Nonsuch Palace and Sunlight House

Nonsuch Palace

Sunlight House

Choose the words

Write the words below in the correct house.

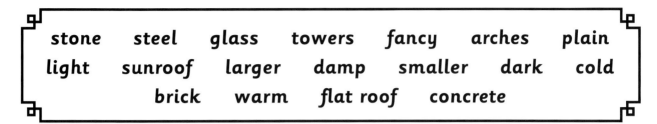

stone   steel   glass   towers   fancy   arches   plain

light   sunroof   larger   damp   smaller   dark   cold

brick   warm   flat roof   concrete

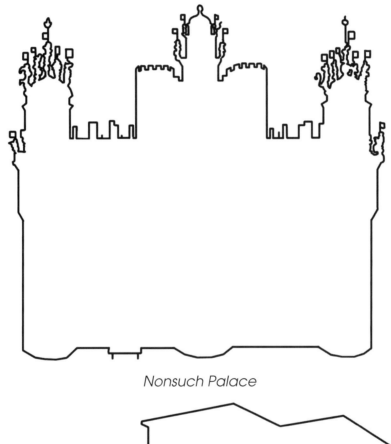

Nonsuch Palace

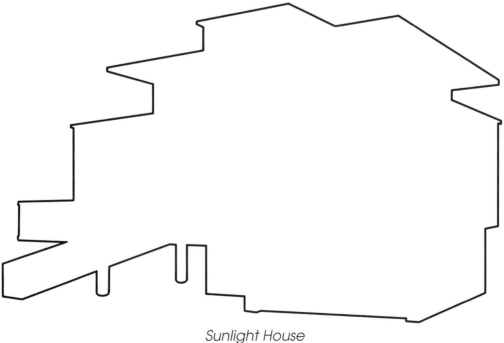

Sunlight House

Living in Nonsuch Palace

Finish the writing frame below in your own words.

I would/would not like to live in Nonsuch Palace.

This is because _____

_____

_____

_____

_____

and also because _____

_____

_____

_____

_____

But not everyone agrees with me. Some people think that

Nonsuch Palace is _____

because _____

_____

_____

_____

_____

_____

Formal Gardens

Background

The Tudor gardens of the great houses were heavily influenced by the Italians. They were formal and corresponded with the straight lines and proportions of the house. Hedges, topiary, fountains, sundials and walkways were common, along with classical statues, columns, and walls with alcoves housing busts. The knot garden (a complex pattern of small hedges) and the maze were also typical features. In between the hedges were neat beds of flowers or herbs. The patterns of the gardens were supposed to be appreciated from above so raised walkways were included in the overall design. The mazes were also complex, but here the hedges were high to increase the difficulty of finding the route out. Water features might include symmetrical ponds or lakes with fountains or statues at their centres. There would be paths leading from the water features, perhaps leading to a summer house. The kitchen gardens and the herb gardens would be found at the rear of the houses.

Using the activity sheets

'The maze'

Once the children have found their way through the maze, they can draw the route with a pencil. Some may like to try designing their own maze using the pattern as a guide.

'Fountains and summer houses'

This is a harder activity sheet which can be completed after the children have a good understanding of the 'The Tudor garden'. The illustration may assist them in completing the activity, and it may be easier if they work in pairs. It is best if they read the passage through and then the labels before filling in the gaps. The answers, in correct order, are as follow: fountains, summer houses, sundial, kitchen garden, herb garden, knot garden, maze.

Working with the resource

'The Tudor garden'

You will need to discuss the following illustration of a Tudor garden with the children, encouraging them to identify a range of features and introducing selected vocabulary, particularly, maze, knot garden, summer house, sundial, kitchen garden and herb garden (all of which are involved in the activity sheet 'Fountains and summer houses'). Some children may have visited Hampton Court or Hever Castle and be able to contribute their own experiences.

Useful questions

1 What do you notice first about the Tudor garden?
2 In what shapes are some of the hedges cut?
3 Can you find the maze? What is it for?
4 Which do you think is the knot garden? How were people able to see the pattern?
5 Can you find the sundial? What was it used for?
6 Most Tudor gardens had a herb garden. Why do you think this was?
7 What kind of water features are there?
8 Where would people sit in the summer?

The Tudor garden

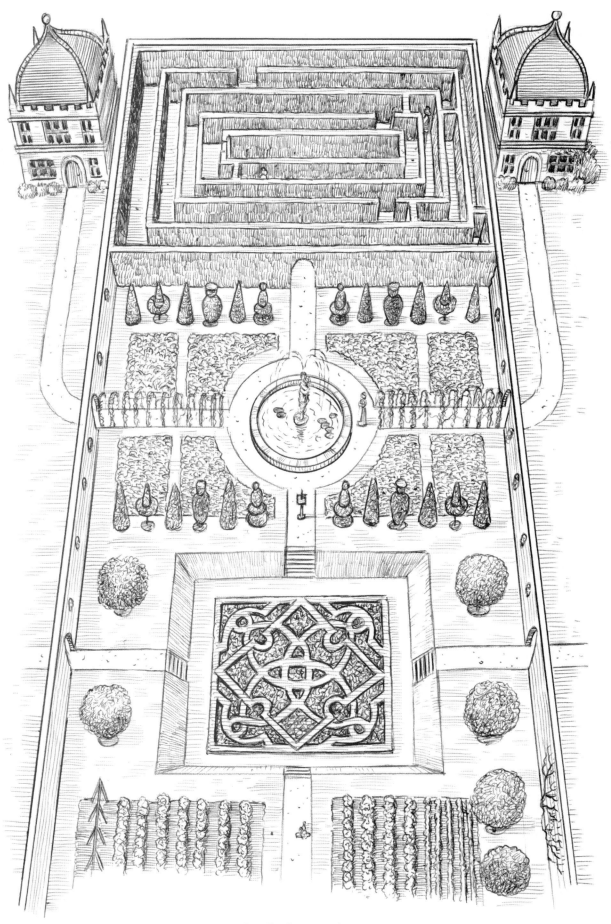

The Tudor garden

The maze

Grand Tudor houses often had a maze. This is a kind of puzzle made from many hedges and paths. When you walk into it, it is very hard to find your way out.

Can you find your way to the middle of this maze and then out?

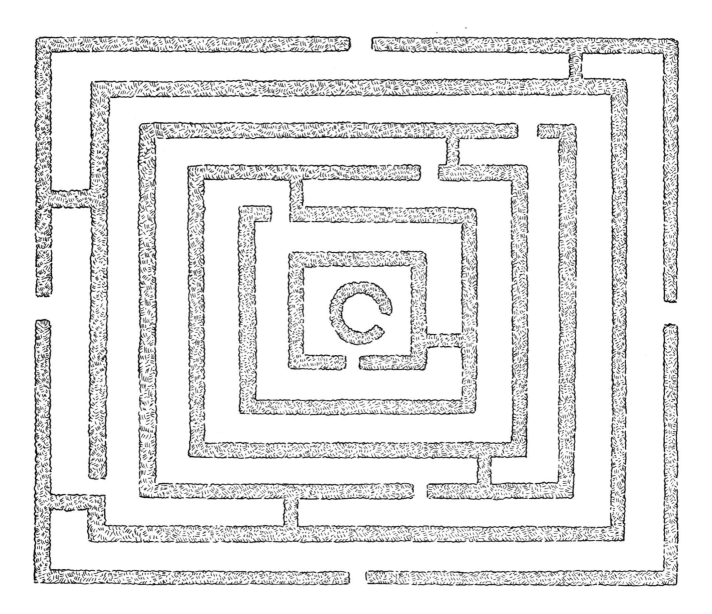

Fountains and summer houses

Read about the Tudor garden below. Then write the correct words, which are listed at the bottom of this page, in the right places.

The Tudor garden was very neat. It had many patterns. These were made of paths and hedges. There were _____ that spouted water. There were_____ _____ where you could sit when the weather was warm. You could also work out the time by looking at the _____ . In the _____ _____ there were fruit and vegetables. There was a _____ _____ too. The herbs were hung up to dry and used in cooking. They were also used as medicines. The _____ _____ had many low hedges. They were shaped in a twisted pattern. But the _____ had high hedges. Can you guess why?

herb garden   knot garden   fountains   kitchen garden

summer houses   maze   sundial

The Kitchen and the Table

Background

Throughout the Tudor period wealthy noblemen had vast retinues of servants. The clerk to the kitchen managed the staff. The yeomen would be responsible for preparing meat to pass to the cooks and other similar tasks while, lower down, the kitchen hands might work in the scullery or the dairy while the peasants cut the corn. Serving at table required another elaborate series of servants. (The beefeater's role, for example, was to taste the meat ensuring it was safe for the monarch.)

Meat was the preferred food. Fine wines were imported and drunk in great quantities. Some fruit and root vegetables were eaten but raw fruit was often associated with fever and plague. Soft fruits, however, were introduced into estate gardens. Oranges, lemons and quinces were imported from Spain and Portugal.

Musicians and masques often accompanied suppers, after which the guests would attend the banqueting suite, which was decked with flowers. These housed a range of sweetmeats set out on sugar plates (see the resource 'Sugar plates') or posy mats (decorated trenchers).

You may wish to discuss the following vocabulary: capon, pheasant, wooden trencher, posy mat, pewter, sweetmeat, rosewater, gelatine, knead, copper, basin.

Using the activity sheet

'Sugar plates'

On the activity sheet, the children are asked to sequence the recipe in correct order. They should look for the number cues: 'First', 'Second', 'Third', 'Fourth', 'Fifth', 'Sixth', and 'Last of all'. They should also grasp that sugar plates are edible. You may wish to try making the recipe with the children, who may then decorate them. They were often etched with patterns or embossed with leaves and fruit.

Working with the resources

The two resource pages should be used together.

'The Tudor kitchen'

Here the focus is on how the food was cooked, the jobs that were done and the utensils that were used.

'A rich supper'

The children can note that the foods prepared in the kitchen are now on the table.

Useful questions

'The Tudor kitchen'

1 Do you think this kitchen belongs to a rich or poor person? Why?
2 What food is cooking? How is it being cooked?
3 What jobs are the people doing?
4 What do you think the jugs, pans and bowls are made of?
5 Which dishes would the meat be served on?
6 What do you think the guests will drink?

'A rich supper'

1 What kind of food do you think rich Tudors liked best?
2 How do they hold their napkins?
3 Can you guess what objects are kept in their hats? What would they use these for?
4 What do you think they did with the bones?
5 How is the meal different from the food you eat?

The Tudor kitchen

The Tudor kitchen

A rich supper

A rich supper

Sugar plates

After the main meal rich Tudors ate sweet things. They laid them out on sugar plates. These plates were made from:

- sugar
- egg white
- lemon juice
- rosewater
- gelatine (which is sticky)

Number the recipe for sugar plates in the right order. The first has been done for you.

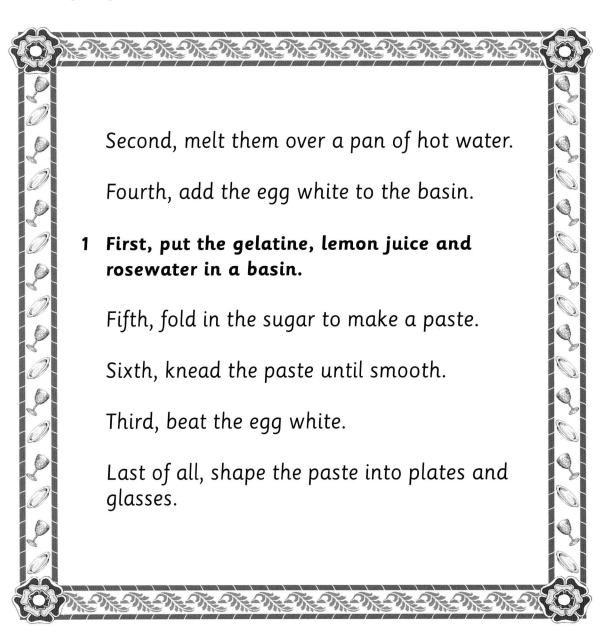

Second, melt them over a pan of hot water.

Fourth, add the egg white to the basin.

1 First, put the gelatine, lemon juice and rosewater in a basin.

Fifth, fold in the sugar to make a paste.

Sixth, knead the paste until smooth.

Third, beat the egg white.

Last of all, shape the paste into plates and glasses.

Henry VIII and the Joust

Background

Henry VIII liked people to consider him as cultured, chivalrous and a man of action. The joust, perhaps, satisfied all three. It harked back to the high age of chivalry during the Middle Ages to the Arthurian legends which Henry would almost certainly have read.

During the joust, opponents were not expected to inflict injury, though it was a dangerous sport nonetheless. At one time Hampton Court included a tiltyard, where Henry practised and performed jousting. Tudor armour for jousts or tournaments was heavy, sometimes over 40 kilograms. The 'horned helmet' was part of a suit of armour that no longer exists.

Working with the resources

'Henry's "horned helmet"' and 'Jousting in the tiltyard'

You may wish to discuss with the children the following vocabulary before beginning either of the resource pages: armour, joust, tiltyard, lance, squire, and point out that the suit of armour does not belong to Henry's 'horned helmet'.

'Henry's "horned helmet"'

The children could speculate about why the helmet has horns. The glasses on the helmet are another oddity; they suggest that Henry was short-sighted and you could use this point to explain that evidence from the past often provides unexpected information.

Useful questions

'Henry's "horned helmet"'

1 Do you know what a suit of armour is?
2 When and why would Henry wear one?
3 What do you think it was like to wear?
4 What do you think it was made of?
5 What decoration does the helmet have?
6 Can you see the glasses? What might the glasses on the helmet tell you about Henry?

'Jousting in the tiltyard'

Guide the children to help them interpret the picture.

1 What is the horseman wearing?
2 What do you think is happening in the picture?
3 What do you think the two men (the squires) on the left are doing?
4 Who do you think is watching?

Using the activity sheet

'The joust'

The children should then sequence the sentences on the activity sheet as follow: 'First', 'Next', 'Then', 'He tries', 'He uses', 'Sometimes'.

You may like to follow up this unit by asking the children to find out more about jousting.

Henry's 'horned helmet'

*Henry's 'horned helmet'
and a suit of armour*

PRIMARY SPECIALS! *Tudor Times*

Jousting in the tiltyard

Jousting in the tiltyard

Source: *Victoria and Albert Museum, Crown copyright, 1510*

The joust

Henry VIII loved to joust. He thought of himself as a knight in shining armour. At Hampton Court he had a space made for jousting. It was called a tiltyard. It was long and narrow with a fence down the middle. People watched the joust from the surrounding towers.

- Put these sentences in order to say what is happening.
- Number them 1 to 6.
- The first has been done for you.

	Next the squires help Henry on to his horse.
1	First everyone sits down to watch the joust.
	He tries to knock the other knight off his horse.
	He uses his lance to do this.
	Then Henry charges down one side of the tiltyard.
	Sometimes the lances would break into pieces.

Other Pastimes

Background

The entertainment that people pursued varied according to their social status. The nobles hunted wild boar and deer. Shooting and fishing were also popular, and Henry VIII frequently used his many estates as hunting grounds. Falconry and fencing as well as jousting or tilting (see 'Henry VIII and the Joust') were also practised by the wealthy. Gambling or gaming was widespread across the classes. Cards, dice and backgammon were popular and large sums of money could exchange hands. Bear-baiting and cock- and dogfighting were also common, as was the more benign bowls. During the Tudors' reign parliament proclaimed against cards and dice, which were thought to encourage dissolute behaviour, at least among the lower classes. Houses used for these purposes were prohibited and fines imposed. Henry VIII along with his nobles continued to enjoy gambling openly, although on certain feast days even they were supposed not to play.

Using the activity sheets

'Tudor games'

Many of our modern games date back through history and the children might note this. The sheet should also give you some idea of whether or not they have any sense of how long ago the Tudor period was.

'Fact or point of view?'

The children need to know the difference between a fact and a point of view, and you can use this sheet to explain the difference.

Working with the resource

'Gambling'

Certain types of gambling, as shown in the illustration, should be easily recognisable, such as cards and dice, and the children may identify billiards as snooker or pool. You will probably need to explain that the other two shown are backgammon and cockfighting. You could also point out that the Tudors' attitude to animals was less humane than our own and that cruelty was common (though not necessarily practised by all Tudors).

Useful questions

Once the children are clear about what each picture shows, you could ask the following questions:

1 Who is playing?
2 How can you tell that they are playing for money?
3 What do you think the birds are doing? Why? What does this picture tell you about how the Tudor's treated animals?
4 Why do you think the man is carrying a bell?

Gambling

Gambling

Tudor games

As well as gambling, rich Tudors liked sport. They played tennis and trained and flew hawks, which are birds of prey. This is called falconry. They also hunted wild boar (wild pig), deer and other animals.

1 Make a list of all the Tudor games you know. It has been started for you.

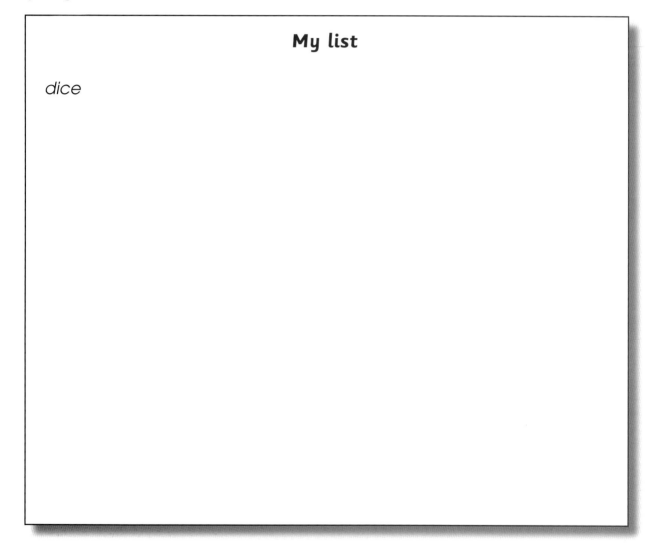

My list

dice

2 Now underline in red all the Tudor games that we still play today.

3 How long have these games lasted since Tudor times? Circle one of the answers below.

50 years   100 years   500 years

Fact or point of view?

Tick the box that you think is the right answer for each question.

	Fact	Point of view
1 Rich Tudors hunted wild animals for sport.	☐	☐
2 I think the Tudors should not have hunted animals because it was cruel.	☐	☐
3 Women as well as men hunted and gambled.	☐	☐
4 Some people lost money at gambling.	☐	☐
5 Servants could not gamble. This is unfair because their masters could.	☐	☐
6 Rich Tudors played tennis.	☐	☐

Write down one more fact that you know about the Tudors.

Fact

Then write a point of view you have about them.

My point of view

Markets and Fairs

Background

Markets and fairs were mainly places of trade; most of those that survived the Tudor period were previously well established. Permission for new markets or fairs would not be granted if the trade of an existing one might be damaged.

A fair, unlike a market, was held yearly usually on the feast day of a particular saint, and it might run from one day to a week. Horse, sheep, goose and various other fairs were held across England, and certain places became known for certain produce. Fairs were also places of entertainment. Music and dancing took place, and there was a considerable amount of alcohol drunk; so much so that fairs became known for their rowdiness. Acrobats and strolling players were often present. When the Thames froze over, during the sixteenth and seventeenth centuries, fairs were also held on the ice.

Bartholomew Fair, named after the saint, began in the twelfth century and lasted until the nineteenth. Miracle plays and mysteries were performed there. Later in the Tudor period it became the focus of Ben Jonson's satire *Bartholomew Fair*.

'What's going on?'

The children should try to classify all the activities in 'The Tudor fair' by completing the questions in the 'spidergram' as follow:
What are people selling? Food – pies, bread, cheese, meat, ale, geese in a pen.
What games are they playing? Dice and bowls.
What is the entertainment? Juggling, tumbling, acting, music, dancing.
What else is going on? Stealing, fighting and any other features noticed.

Working with the resource

'The Tudor fair'

The children should try to spot all the activities in the illustration and you could discuss what these involve. Ale was likely to be the main drink. Note, also, the pickpocket, strolling players and jugglers. You might also like to point to the group playing bowls (and refer to the unit 'Other Pastimes').

Useful questions

1 What kind of food are the people eating?
2 What do you think they are drinking?
3 What are the people doing on the cart?
4 Do you know what instrument the musician is playing?
5 One person in the picture is not going to be very happy! Can you tell why? (The person having his pocket picked.)
6 How many other activities can you see?
7 Have you ever been to a fair? How was it different? How was it the same?

Using the activity sheets

'Fairs, fetes and theme parks'

Most children will have been to at least one of these and should be able to compare the Tudor fair with their own experiences. Any who have not, could work with a partner who has. In addition to the example given, similarities might include: food and drink on sale, people enjoying themselves and music playing. Dissimilarities might be the differences in entertainment, entry fees, and no animals for sale.

The Tudor fair

The Tudor fair

PRIMARY SPECIALS!: *Tudor Times*

What's going on?

People went to fairs to enjoy themselves and to buy and sell goods.

Using the picture 'The Tudor fair' answer the questions in the 'spidergram' below.

What are people selling?   **What games are they playing?**

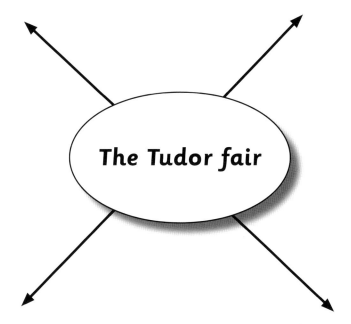

The Tudor fair

What is the entertainment?   **What else is going on?**

What would you like to find out more about?

How would you go about it?

Fairs, fetes and theme parks

Choose one of the following:

A fair   **A theme park**   **A school fete or fair**

Compare it to a Tudor fair. The chart has been started for you.

The same as a Tudor fair	Not the same as a Tudor fair
Lots of people all together.	

Which would you prefer to go to?

Why?

The Elizabethan Theatre

Background

Both rich and poor attended the theatre in large numbers. The wealthy had seats in the galleries. The groundlings stood in the pit and, while open to the elements, were closer to the stage. Food and drink would be handed round among the audience, who would readily show their displeasure if they did not enjoy a play. There was a range of special effects; fireworks were sometimes let off on stage to signify a thunderbolt, and pig's blood was often used to represent human blood. Actors could be lowered from the 'heavens' with the use of a winch or appear through the stage trapdoor. Often there was a musical accompaniment. Minor players or the clown might sing, and a burlesque, perhaps with a fiddle or drum, was frequently presented at the end. Although the theatre was popular with Elizabeth it was not with Parliament, and troupes of actors were required to hold licences. Theatres were closed at times of epidemics, and there were those who thought them sufficiently sinful to be the cause of plague.

Using the activity sheets

'Drums and fireworks'

Here the children should match the Tudor props and special effects to their uses.

'Crab the Dog'

Clowns or comic turns in a play were popular. Shakespeare includes Crab the Dog in *The Two Gentlemen of Verona* and though the dog's presence had a serious purpose it nonetheless provided humour. The children should have sufficient information on the page to complete the bill.

Working with the resource

'Watching a play'

The children should be able to answer most of the questions below by studying the illustration. The trumpeter's job was to herald the beginning of the play and call the audience to the theatre. The tiring house, where the actors changed, was at the back of the stage, where props could also be kept. Placards would be used to signal changes of scene. You could point out to the children that female roles were played by boys. You might also like to explain what 'props' are, discuss the special effects used and the musical or acrobatic performances, in preparation for the activity sheets.

Useful questions

1 Where is the stage? What is it like?
2 Can you guess where the 'heavens' were?
3 Where do you think the actors changed?
4 Where did the rich sit?
5 If you had a cheap ticket you had a place in the pit. Can you guess where this was?
6 People in the pit were called groundlings. What do you think it was like to be a groundling?
7 The trumpeter had a special job. Can you guess what it was?

Watching a play

Watching a play

Drums and fireworks

What do you think these Tudor props were used for? Match them to their uses by drawing a line.

Prop	Use
drums rolling	to fight with
a trapdoor in the roof with a rope	a stream
	for a king or queen
sword	
	a door
a trapdoor in the stage	
	a death
wings	
	for an angel or god to appear
fireworks	
	lightning
animal blood in a bag	
water running	for an angel
crown	for a ghost to appear
curtain	thunder

Crab the Dog

William Shakespeare was a famous Tudor playwright. Crab the Dog appeared in one of his plays, *The Two Gentlemen of Verona*. When a play was to be performed, bills would be given out to announce it. These were rather like flyers or posters.

Finish this bill about Crab the Dog.
Use the information on this page to help you.
Then draw a picture of Crab the Dog and a Tudor pattern around the bill.

Crab the Dog

Performing at The Curtain

In the play _____

By _____

To take place on

_____

At

_____

To be followed by

_____

And also

_____

> **Useful words**
>
> bells   drums   fiddles   jugglers   acrobats   tumblers

Tudor Education

Background

In Tudor England, children were regarded as miniature adults. Those from peasant families had to earn their living and contribute to the family income from a young age. Orphans might be looked after by villagers or by the parish but the children of the very poor often had to fend for themselves. Only boys from wealthy families received a formal education, while a few girls were taught at home by tutors. The grammar school, where the sons of the merchant classes were educated (and occasionally poorer boys), might only have one master. The more prestigious would have two: the grammaticus, who taught the older boys, and the submagister, who minded the younger pupils. The grammaticus controlled the class with the use of a cane, sometimes shown as a birch. Latin grammar was taught and the use of English discouraged. Divinity and singing were also taught.

Using the activity sheets

'Then and now'

Once the children have completed this activity sheet they can talk together about the differences between the Tudor school and their own. They might also like to note any similarities (such as the study of music and religion, and the mid-day break). This will also prepare them for the following sheet.

'The Tudor school: my point of view'

The children can use the frame on this sheet to sum up their views and what they have learned about the Tudor school. It is useful if the previous activity and resource sheet are available for them to refer to.

Working with the resource

'The Tudor school'

If the children study the picture closely they will note several features that will help them with the activity sheets, such as the subjects being taught and the equipment being used. The younger boys are learning the alphabet or scripture from a hornbook; this was a wooden board with a handle and contained printed paper (which was expensive) covered with a thin sheet of animal horn to protect the pages. Other equipment in the picture includes chalk and slates for the younger boys, and the older boys are using quill pens, ink and paper. The master's cane should help them deduce how the pupils were controlled and that attending school was unlikely to be a pleasant experience.

Useful questions

1 Who is being educated? (You might need to point out that there are no girls present.)
2 What are the boys on the bench reading from?
3 What are they writing with? Find more than one thing.
4 What other lesson is going on?
5 What do you think the teachers were like? Look carefully at the picture!

The Tudor school

The Tudor school

Then and now

Working with a partner, read the list under 'A Tudor school' below. Then write a list about your school under 'My school'.

A Tudor school	My school
Lessons	**Lessons**
Reading	
Writing	
Bible Study	
Latin	
Singing	
Music	
School times	**School times**
Summer	**Summer**
6:00am – 11:00am 1:00pm – 5:00pm	
Winter	**Winter**
7:00am – 11:00am 1:00pm – 4:00pm	
Equipment	**Equipment**
Hornbook	
Slate and chalk	
Quill	
Ink pot	
Knife for sharpening quill	

The Tudor school: my point of view

Finish the writing frame below. Use the work you have already done to help you.

I think the worst thing about Tudor schools is _____

_____

Tudor schools were different from schools today in many ways.

Firstly _____

_____

Secondly _____

_____

Thirdly _____

_____

But they were the same in some ways too. For example

_____

_____

_____

_____

And one good thing about them was _____

_____

_____

_____

_____

Farming and Enclosures

Background

Most of the population in Tudor England worked on the land and were highly dependent on the land-owning classes from whom they rented small strips of land to grow food. However, the economic conditions of the Tudor period, which included rising prices and bad harvests, meant that more and more landowners turned away from growing wheat to sheep farming, so some peasants lost their strips of land. The woollen industry was expanding and the wool could be sold abroad. Some landowners also enclosed common land for sheep grazing, denying the peasants the right to graze their animals. The accumulative effect of this was an increase in poverty. Sources record that particularly the aged and the sick were affected, and there were more people unemployed. In addition, there was an increase in the population. These factors, along with the dissolution of the monasteries under Henry VIII, meant that it fell to the parishes to support the increasing numbers of poor, many of whom became vagrants.

Using the activity sheet

'Landowners and villagers'

When the children have completed this sheet you should have an idea of whether or not they have grasped the basic effects of enclosure on the peasants. (Sentences 1, 4, 5, 7, and 8 are correct and sentences 2, 3 and 6 are incorrect.) The children could work in pairs to discuss their answers.

Working with the resources

The two resource pages should be used together.

'Working on the land'

This depicts a farming scene that shows the relationship between the land-owning class and the peasants who worked for them before the land was enclosed. You can use the questions to encourage the children to recognise how much the peasants were dependent on the landowner.

'Fencing in the land'

This presents the same picture after enclosure of the land. The children need to grasp the causal relationships between enclosing land and the increase in the numbers of poor.

Useful questions

'Working on the land'

1 Do you think most villagers were rich or poor? Why do you think this?
2 Who do you think the villages rented land from?
3 Where did they grow food?
4 What kind of things did they have to give the squire?
5 Where did their animals graze?
6 What do you think 'common land' means?

'Fencing in the land'

1 What has happened to the land?
2 Why was it hard for the villagers to grow food?
3 Why did the landowner build fences or hedges?
4 What do you think happened to the villagers and their animals?

Working on the land

Working on the land

Fencing in the land

Fencing in the land

Landowners and villagers

Read the following sentences.
Tick the 'true' box beside the ones that are true.
Put a cross in the 'false' box beside the ones that are not true.

		True	False
1	Some landowners grazed sheep instead of growing wheat.	☐	☐
2	Some landowners grew flowers instead of growing wheat.	☐	☐
3	The villagers took over all the land.	☐	☐
4	The villagers had no strips of land to grow food.	☐	☐
5	The landowners built fences around the common land.	☐	☐
6	The villagers stole all the wool.	☐	☐
7	Some villagers tore down the fences.	☐	☐
8	The villagers became poorer.	☐	☐

Poverty and Beggars

Background

The major social problem of the Tudor period was poverty. The poor were divided into two classes: the deserving and the undeserving. The former, the very young, elderly and sick, could elicit some sympathy and by law some provision. (Householders had to pay a rate to the parish under the poor laws of 1597 and 1601.) Some wealthy families built alms-houses. Giving charity to the deserving poor was part of Christian belief and conferred status on the family.

The undeserving poor were largely seen as criminals. With the rise in unemployment many of the poor took to the road in search of work and some became vagrants. Some earned their living by theft and deception, often resorting to a range of ingenious tactics, from feigning illness and injury to the ploys of the 'courtesy man' or confidence trickster. Laws were harsh and punishments severe. Beggars were treated especially harshly if caught stealing, often being hung. Other forms of punishment might include public ridicule, such as the stocks and the pillory, or whipping and branding.

Working with the resource

'Rich and poor'

This resource, which depicts a wealthy citizen and a beggar, can encourage the children to speculate about what is actually happening – are alms being given or not? You can use the source to illustrate that information in historical sources can sometimes be difficult to interpret. You could also ask the children if we have beggars today (see question 6 below), explaining that while some things change over time, others stay the same.

Useful questions

1 When do you think the picture was drawn? Why?
2 Who is in the picture?
3 How are the two people different from each other?
4 What are they wearing?
5 What is happening? Why?
6 Do we see people begging today?

Using the activity sheets

'Who? What? Why?'

This activity sheet supports the discussion points arising from the resource page and the children can record the information in the boxes. Under 'What is happening?'/'Why is it happening?' they could decide which answer is the best or record more than one answer.

'Begging'

Here the emphasis is on how the poor attempted to survive. The children could work alone or with a partner to complete the passage. The correct order of words is: food, work, stole, sell, soap, froth, mad.

Rich and poor

Rich and poor

Source: *Reproduced from the Maunsell Collection*

PRIMARY SPECIALS!: *Tudor Times*

Who? What? Why?

Who is in the picture?	**What do they look like?**
What is happening?	**Why is it happening?**

Begging

Read the sentences below first.
Then fill in the gaps with the right words from underneath.

When there was no _____ to eat people began

to beg. They went from place to place and had no

homes. Some tried to find _____ to do. But

there was very little work. Some _____ food.

Some stole goods to _____ . Some beggars even

ate _____ ! This made them _____

at the mouth. That way people would think they were

_____ and feel sorry for them. Then they might

give them money.

work   food   froth   mad   sell   soap   stole

Plague and Fever

Background

As hygiene was poor, disease was rife in Tudor England. Plagues were common and there were several serious epidemics between 1563 and 1603, which killed thousands of people (though nothing as severe as either the Black Death of 1348 or the Great Plague of 1665). Unaware that bubonic plague was spread by rats' fleas, many believed that it was a judgement from God, or spread by domestic animals, birds, damp or odours. The poor were usually the first to suffer and the rich, better nourished, had greater defences and could escape the towns and cities when it struck. There were many other infections too. Pneumonic plague, which attacked the lungs, was spread by coughing while smallpox, typhus, measles and tuberculosis were endemic. In London the bills of mortality published each week listed conditions such as, 'sweating sickness', 'pox' and 'flux' (dysentery). The 'ague' (malaria) was also a common fever, since mosquitoes were attracted to the rivers and open sewers.

Using the activity sheets

'Yes or no?'

Here the children are asked to identify correct information about the plague, how it was spread and how the Tudors dealt with it. The children should tick the 'Yes' box for questions 2, 3, 4, 7, 9 and 10 and the 'No' box for the remainder.

'Plague diary'

The children can complete a simple entry using the frame and the list of useful words. They may also add any extra information that they have learned. You may wish to point out that 1603, the date of the diary entry, was the year of Elizabeth's death and the end of the Tudor period.

Working with the resource

'Swellings and plague spots'

The illustration should help the children to note the symptoms of bubonic plague – high temperature, sickness, painful swellings (buboes) in the neck and armpit, and haemorrhages under the skin (plague spots). There are also indications that the victims could be treated. The cautery, used for piercing the swellings, has a long handle so that the doctor was able to keep his distance from the patient. The plague mask, also used for protection, is filled with herbs. There are also herbs hanging in the room. Explain the relationship between the rat, the bundle of clothes (harbouring rat fleas) and the transmission of the disease to humans. You could also point out that Tudor knowledge of medicine was unsophisticated compared with our own and was based on a different set of values.

Useful questions

1 How can you tell that someone is sick? What are his symptoms?
2 What disease do you think he has?
3 Who is treating the patient? What is he wearing? Why?
4 How is the patient being treated?
5 Can you guess how the patient became ill?
6 Think of ways that treatment is different today.

Swellings and plague spots

Swellings and plague spots

PRIMARY SPECIALS!: *Tudor Times*

Yes or no?

Read the sentences about the plague.
Tick the 'yes' box beside the ones that are true.
Put a cross in the 'no' box beside the ones that are not true.

		Yes	**No**
1	A sign of the plague was small pimples.	☐	☐
2	A sign of the plague was painful swellings.	☐	☐
3	The swellings were called buboes.	☐	☐
4	The plague was spread by rat fleas.	☐	☐
5	The plague was spread by damp and mist.	☐	☐
6	Tudor doctors knew how to get rid of the plague.	☐	☐
7	The Tudors did not know how the plague was spread.	☐	☐
8	A plague mask was worn by the patient.	☐	☐
9	A plague mask was worn by the doctor.	☐	☐
10	A cautery was used to pierce the swellings.	☐	☐

Plague diary

Pretend you are a child living in Tudor times. Someone living near you has caught the plague. Use the writing frame and the words below to finish the diary entry.

18 July 1603

Terrible news! Today I heard that _____

_____

The doctor came but would not stay long. He came to _____

_____

He wore _____

And carried _____

Some people say that the plague is caused by _____

_____

Others say _____

_____

Mother tells me that we must _____

_____

| plague spots | pierce | swellings | mask | herbs | cautery |
| long handle | birds | dogs | cats | God | damp | smells |

Tudor Medicine

Background

Tudor medicine was based on the idea that if the four 'humours' – black bile, yellow bile, blood and phlegm – were out of balance the body became sick. Humours were also character types (melancholic, choleric, sanguine, phlegmatic), the elements (earth, fire, water, air), the seasons, and mixes of other attributes such as cold, dry, hot and moist, all of which could be taken into account in diagnosis. Leeches were used to draw 'bad blood' and hot cups, sometimes containing scalding cloths, were applied over sores to draw pus. Herbs were used, sometimes successfully, and were often chosen because they shared the same properties as the disease. For example, poppies could be used to cure a red rash. Superstition was widespread and a variety of charms were available. There were also several kinds of doctors. Physicians were scholars, barber surgeons performed amputations (as well as cutting hair!), and apothecaries mixed potions. 'Wise women' with a knowledge of herbs were available to the poorer classes and there were quacks who charged lower rates.

Using the activity sheets

'Tools and medicines'

The children need to complete the fact file by either adding the names of the missing equipment or the functions. The missing equipment is in order as follows: urine flask, leeches, scalpel, pestle and mortar. The missing functions are: for putting on sores or rashes, piercing plague swellings (buboes), drawing out pus, making cures (or spells), making amputations.

'Mix a potion'

Once the children have discussed and understood the examples shown on the resource page they can select information on the sheet to complete 'Mix a potion'.

Working with the resource

'A visit to the doctor'

Discuss with the children the contents of the picture. It includes equipment used by various types of doctors; there is a urine flask together with a pottery ointment jar and ingredient jars. The potions would be available from the apothecary. The barber surgeon's tools include various pliers, a saw, scalpels, knives and a syringe. Leeches are kept in one of the jars and a hot cup is being placed over a wound. There is also a long-handled cautery for piercing buboes (see the previous unit). The female assistant is using a pestle and mortar to mix herbs, which she has possibly picked from those hanging from the shelf. You may wish to label the picture as you discuss it and point out that doctors and surgeons today still use some of the same equipment.

Useful questions

1 Which person in the picture is the doctor? What is he doing? Why?
2 What equipment and medicines might the doctor use?
3 What is the woman doing? Why?
4 What do you think it would be like to be a patient in Tudor times?
5 Do you notice anything else?

A visit to the doctor

A visit to the doctor

Tools and medicines

The fact file below lists a Tudor doctor's tools and medicine. It also says what they were used for. But it is not finished. Fill in the gaps.

Tools and medicines	What they were used for
	for collecting urine
Jars of herbs	*for adding to potions*
Jars of ointment	
Long-handled cautery	
	for sucking out 'bad blood'
Cups	
Book of charms	
Saw	
	for cutting open the skin
	for grinding things into powder

Mix a potion

Quacks were not real doctors. People went to them because they were cheaper.
Pretend you are a Tudor quack. Mix a potion to cure an illness.
Look at 'A visit to the doctor' to help you.

Decide:
- what the illness will be.
- what you will put in the potion.
- when it should be drunk (such as the time of the full moon).

To cure _____

Mix _____

_____

Add _____

_____

Boil with _____

_____

Stir in _____

_____

Drink at the time of _____

_____

Tom's Quest

Background

Most Tudor towns were small. Seaports such as Bristol were growing but London had the largest population. Streets were usually dirty and harboured disease. There were open sewers and no drains, and waste was simply thrown into the street. Rats spread infection. Beggars were numerous and there were many poor children and orphans. Despite this, markets were held and there was considerable trade. There were also street entertainers, musicians and many pickpockets. In London the Thames was heavily used for transport and carrying goods.

The fictitious story, Tom's Quest, should give the children some idea of what a Tudor town was like and they may be able to bring their own knowledge to bear, for example by providing further information about the plague.

Using the activity sheet

'Tom's life and my life'

The children can use the compare and contrast sheet to note the differences between Tom's life and their own. You can use the answers they give to the final questions, 'Do you think any children today live like Tom?' and 'How do you know?' to raise issues about child poverty, pointing out that in history some things change, while others stay the same.

Working with the resource

'Tom's quest'

It is best if you read the story to the children who can follow it from their own copy. The questions focus on the main characters and the situation Tom finds himself in. If the children read between the lines, perhaps with assistance from you, they should be able to deduce that Tom is a beggar or street urchin and Mistress Paxton has been kind to him in the past. Once the children realise that Tom and the old man have come upon the plague, they can speculate about what might happen next. They can also guess what has happened to Mistress Paxton.

You may wish to discuss the following vocabulary before you begin, or you could ask the children to guess by using the context of the story: quest, tavern, cobbles, pippin, jerkin, breeches, doublet, mistress, ferryman.

Useful questions

1 Who is Tom? What is he like?
2 What is Tom doing?
3 What does the old man think Tom is?
4 Why is Tom sorry for the old man?
5 What does he offer to do for Tom?
6 Who is Mistress Paxton? What do you think she is like?
7 Why do you think the pie shop is closed and there is no one around?

You might also like to discuss the differences between Tom's life and that of the children, in preparation for the activity sheet.

Tom's quest

Tom crept along the side-wall near the tavern. He was cold and wet and his hair hung down over his dark eyes. He wore no shoes but the soles of his feet were hard, so sharp little stones did not hurt him. People were everywhere, buying and selling, laughing or squabbling. A man dragging a small hand-cart behind him pushed past. The cart bumped over the cobbles and a red pippin fell out and rolled away. In a second Tom was there. He snatched it up and tucked it into his jerkin. He had not eaten a pippin in a long time. It must be a lucky omen.

As he came into the lane the stench from the slops hit his nostrils. The houses were huddled together and seemed to tilt towards him. Tom felt as if they were asking him, 'What right has a ruffian like you to visit us?'

'I'm searching for Mistress Paxton's house,' he said out loud firmly.

A man standing nearby had been watching him. 'Well young beggar, have you lost your way?' Tom turned around. An old gentleman in breeches, doublet and a feathered hat was standing beside him. He had seen better days. 'New to this part?' he continued.

'And what's it to you?' replied Tom. But seeing that the man was blind he felt sorry for him and was less afraid.

'I'm in search of Mistress Paxton,' he repeated. 'She's opened a pie shop hereabouts.'

A rat scuttled across his foot and vanished.

'And what would a scoundrel like you want with Mistress Paxton?'

'Food,' said Tom simply.

The old man thought for a moment. 'I believe there is a new pie shop somewhere near the river …'

'Yes, by the river. That's what she said', interrupted Tom.

'It's some distance from here. You won't find your way through these winding lanes. Come with me.'

PRIMARY SPECIALS!: *Tudor Times*

Tom hesitated. Then he took the man's arm and they walked back the bustling way that Tom had come.

It was noon and the sun was peeping from behind a rain cloud. The river sparkled briefly between the alleys as the boy and the blind man made their way south. Tom could see a ferryman plying his trade.

About half an hour later they reached a narrow cobbled street.

'Well, this is it. I'm sure this is it. But don't it feel strange?' said the old man.

Tom nodded. There was barely a sound and not a soul to be seen. He looked up and down the street searching for the pie shop and his eye caught what he was looking for. 'There it is!' he shouted. 'I can see it at the other end.'

They walked on slowly and a little puzzled at the absence of people. A few idle dogs sniffed among some rags piled next to a house. A rat popped its head out from a sewer, darted away and one of the dogs gave chase. Tom glanced down at the rags and immediately froze. The old man sensed his fear. Lying among the rags was a body. It was quite dead and covered in sores. There were swellings under the armpits. Tom gasped. The old man grabbed Tom's arm, 'No place for us here, no place for us here,' he said, dragging Tom away.

They ran along the cobbles not stopping to catch their breath until they reached the end of the street. Tom looked back. He could still see the pie shop. But there was no sign of Mistress Paxton anywhere. The door was locked and the wooden shutters were down. A bright new sign had been put up; it showed a succulent meat pie with a deep pastry crust. Tom stared longingly after it.

Mary Green

Tom's life and my life

Tom's life	My life
Where is Tom's home?	Where is your home?
How does he get food?	How do you get food?
What are his clothes like?	What are your clothes like?
Does Tom go to school?	Do you go to school?
Who helps Tom?	Who helps you?

Do you think any children today live like Tom?

How do you know?